BL 2.2

BY
TONY
NORMAN
ILLUSTRATED BY
ANTHONY
WILLIAMS

FULL FLIG
H
D0511451
Schools Library Service

Titles in the FULL FLIGHT runway series

Level 3

Goal!	Jane A C West
Too Hot	Roger Hurn/Alison Hawes

Level 4

A Big Catch	Alison Hawes
Deyda's Drum	Roger Hurn
The Strawberry Thief	Alison Hawes
Billy's Boy	Melanie Joyce

Level 5

Cage Boy	Jillian Powell
Master Blaster	Melanie Joyce
Game Player King	Stan Cullimore
In the Zone	Tony Norman

Level 6

Dodgems	Jane A C West
Tansy Smith	Helen Orme

Level 7

Pirate Attack	Jonny Zucker
Hitting the Basket	Jonny Zucker

Badger Publishing Limited
Suite G08, Business & Technology Centre
Bessemer Drive, Stevenage, Hertfordshire, SG1 2DX
Telephone: 01438 791037 Fax: 01438 791036
www.badger-publishing.co.uk

In the Zone ISBN 978 1 84691 855 1

Publisher: David Jamieson
Editor: Danny Pearson
Design: Fiona Grant
Illustration: Anthony Williams
Printed and bound in China through Colorcraft Ltd., Hong Kong

Contents

Badger Publishing

Vocabulary

Dream/Dreams
Excited
Hero
Penalty
Shoots
Power

Main Characters

Callum
Top striker for local team the Jays. He dreams of playing for City.

Coach
Coach of Callum's Team

Scout
Works for top team City. Looks for young stars who could play for his club.

Jazz
Plays in goal for the Allstars.

Chapter 1
Dreams Can Come True

Callum is late.

He runs down a city street.

The cold wind stings his face.

Callum has a dream.

One day he will be a top star.

A star striker for City.

City's young star striker lifts the Cup. Oh yes, dreams can come true!
ALLSTAR

Callum plays for the Jays.

He scores most of their goals.

Now the Jays are in the final.

The Jays and the Allstars run out.

Callum's heart beats like a drum.

Is he feeling afraid?

No, he is feeling excited!

Come on Jays!
Come on, we can win this.
Go for it Allstars!
5
7

It's a great game.

Callum is red hot.

His low shot stings the goalie's hands.

A scout from top club City is at the game.

He is on the edge of his seat.

He writes down a name in a small book.

But whose name does he write down?

Chapter 3
Penalty!

Callum is in on goal with two minutes to go.

He gets a kick in the back of the leg.

Penalty!

The ball is on the penalty spot.

The scout is on the edge of his seat.

If Callum scores, he will be a star.

Callum stands alone.

His eyes are on the ball.

He is in the zone.

All eyes are on Callum.

Can he win the Cup for the Jays?

Hero or zero, which will he be?

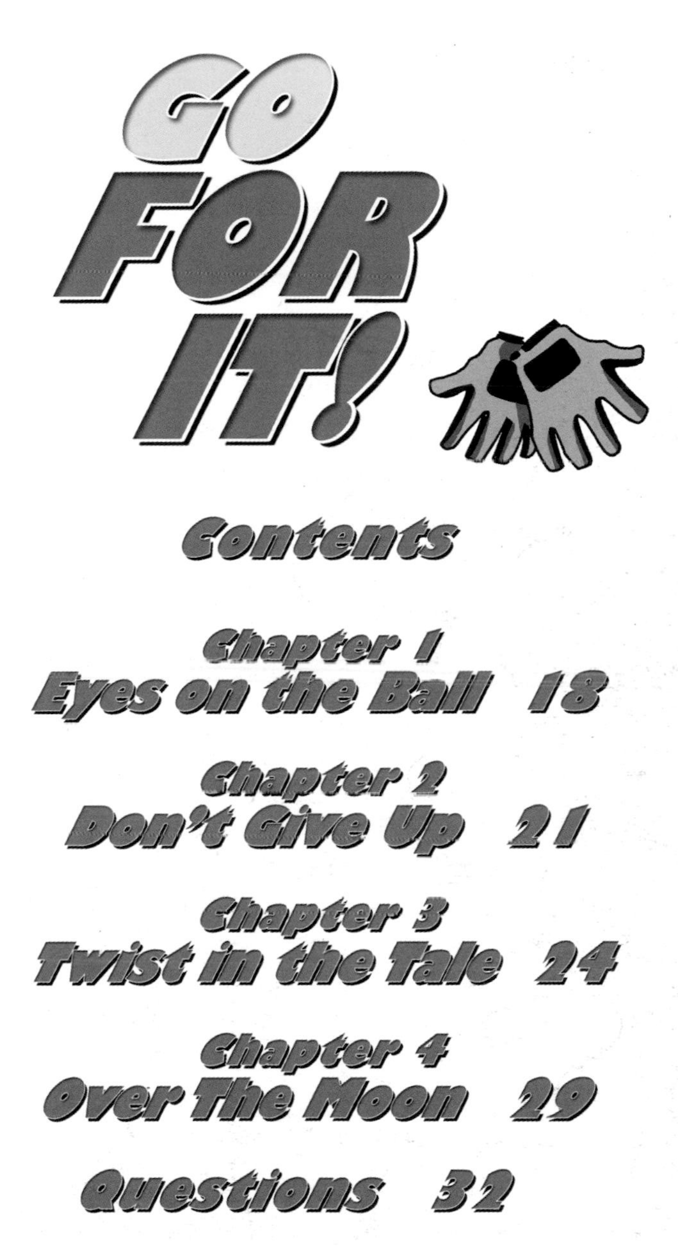

Contents

Chapter 1
Eyes on the Ball

Jazz is in goal for the Allstars.

His eyes are on the ball.

He is in the zone.

Jazz is ready for the penalty.

Callum's kick is full of power.

Jazz dives to his right.

Jazz gets his right hand to the ball.

It flies wide of the post.

What a save!

Chapter 2
Don't Give Up

Jazz jumps to his feet.

Callum does not look like a star now.

A high cross comes into the box.

Jazz easily beats Callum to the ball.

'If he gives up, that's good for us,' Jazz thinks.

Then Callum hears a loud voice.

His coach won't let him give up.

Chapter 3
Twist in the Tale

Callum is back in the game.

He beats two men and shoots for goal.

Jazz pushes the ball
over the bar.

A corner with just seconds to go.

Callum is in the box with his back to goal.

Jazz thinks his goal is safe.

But he is wrong.

Callum will not give up.

The ball flies high into the box.

Callum jumps high into the air.

He kicks the ball back over his head.

The ball hits the back of the net.

The Jays win and Callum is a star!

Jazz shakes hands with Callum.

The scout from City walks up to them.

He wants them both to have a trial at City.

Ten years later…

Callum was right. Dreams can come true!

Questions

What does 'in the zone' mean?

Who is the man writing notes in a small book?

How would you feel if you had to take Callum's penalty? Afraid? Excited?

When Jazz saves the penalty, Callum gives up. Who makes him try again?

How does Callum score the winning goal?

Which club does the football scout come from?